With text and arrangements by Peter Lavender.

START PLAYING KEYBOARD COLLECTION 6

Exclusive distributors:
Music Sales Limited
8/9 Frith Street,
London W1V 5TZ,
England.
Music Sales Pty Limited
120 Rothschild Avenue,
Rosebery, NSW 2018,
Australia.

This book © Copyright 1989 by
Wise Publications
Order No. AM76563
ISBN 0.7119.1976.3

Compiled and arranged by Peter Lavender
Designed by Pearce Marchbank Studio
Cover photograph by Rod Shone
Music processed by Barnes Music Engraving

Music Sales' complete catalogue lists thousands of
titles and is free from your local music shop, or direct from
Music Sales Limited. Please send £1 in stamps for postage to
Music Sales Limited, 8/9 Frith Street, London W1V 5TZ.

Printed in the United Kingdom by
J.B. Offset Printers (Marks Tey) Limited, Marks Tey, Essex.

Wise Publications
London /New York/Sydney

The ABC of SFX Music

In SFX music, the melody is clearly written in large lettered notes. Each note can easily be located on your keyboard and then played with the right hand.

The songs in SFX music books are all written in the following keyboard range. The symbol at the beginning of the music staff is the treble clef, indicating the notes are played with the right hand:

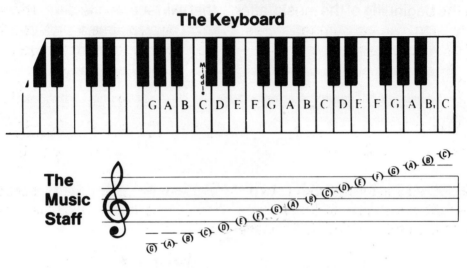

The Sharp Sign (♯) will sometimes appear before a music note. Simply play the *black key* to the *right* of the *white key:*

The Flat Sign (♭) placed before a note tells you to play the *black key* that lies to the *left* of the *white key:*

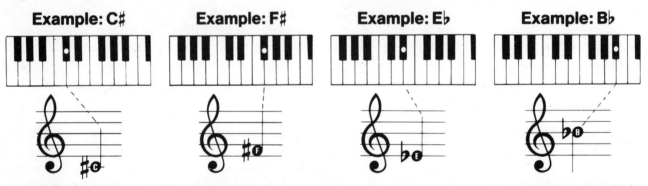

The Music Staff is divided into equal sections by vertical lines called *Bar Lines.* Each section is a *Measure.* The end of a piece of music is marked by a double bar line.

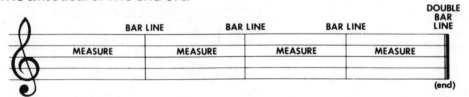

All music is played in time to a *beat.* The six types of notes most often used in SFX music all have a *time value* that relates to the beat:

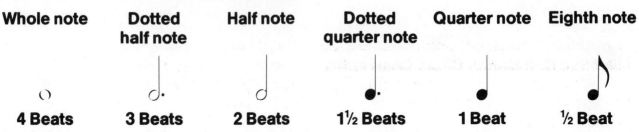

Whole note	Dotted half note	Half note	Dotted quarter note	Quarter note	Eighth note
4 Beats	3 Beats	2 Beats	1½ Beats	1 Beat	½ Beat

The Rest is a silent break in the music. The symbols are written in the staff, and like music notes, rests each have a time value:

Whole rest   **Half rest**   **Quarter rest**   **Eighth rest**
(4 Beats)   (2 Beats)   (1 Beat)   ($\frac{1}{2}$ Beat)

The Time Signature comprises two numbers at the beginning of the music, after the treble clef sign. The top number shows the amount of beats in each measure. The bottom number indicates the type of note that will receive *one* beat. These are the most popular time signatures. The lower number 4 represents the quarter note:

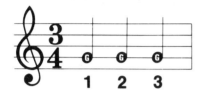

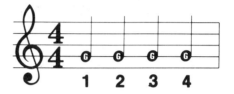

The Tie is a curved line that connects two consecutive notes on the same line or in the same space in the staff. When a tie appears in the music, play the first note and sustain the sound for the *total* time value of the two notes:

Tied Notes

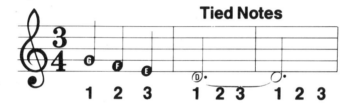

Repeat Signs are two dots alongside double bar lines. They indicate that all the music in between the pairs of repeat signs is to be played through again:

Quite often there will only be one repeat sign at the end of a passage of music. The repeat is then made from the very beginning:

Double Endings are sections of music with staff repeat signs. 1st and 2nd time brackets above the staff indicate where a short 'skip' is to be made in the music after the repeat has been played:

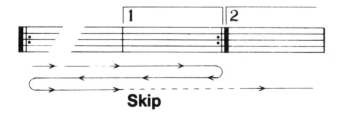

Skip

Left Hand Keyboard Accompaniment. SFX music has Major and Minor chords clearly written above the staff. The optional 'seventh' type of chord is shown with the 7 outside the chord frame:

Your keyboard Owner's Manual will explain how these chords are played with your left hand.

Conventional (Fingered) Chords can also be used. **The SFX Master Chord Chart** in this book shows the most practical chord positions for this type of left hand accompaniment.

Right Hand Fingering
Always use recommended fingering when indicated in SFX music.

After The Ball

Words & Music by Charles K. Harris

Suggested Registration: Strings or Trumpet

Rhythm: Waltz

Tempo: Fast

Technique: Dotted quarter notes

Sharps. ♯

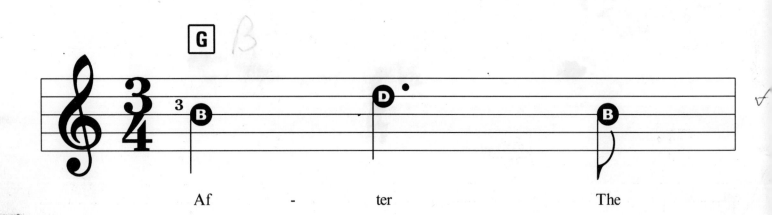

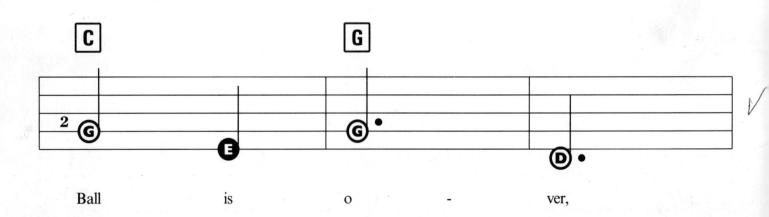

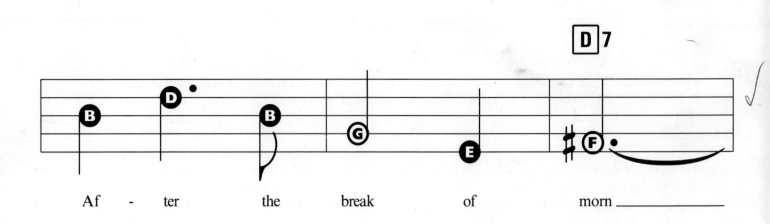

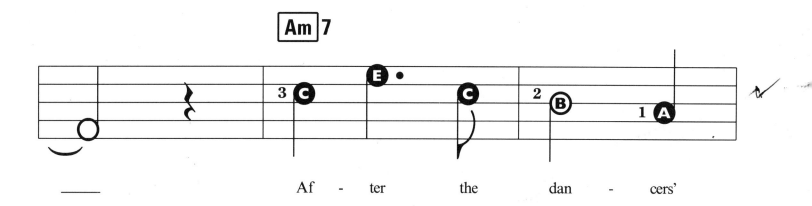

Af - ter the dan - cers'

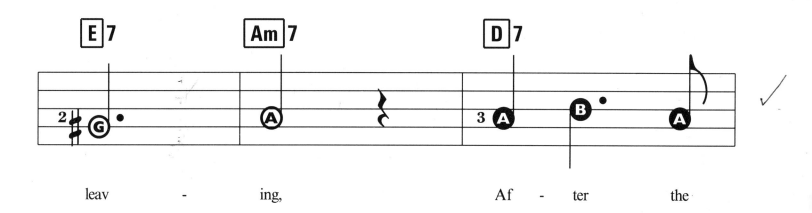

leav - ing, Af - ter the

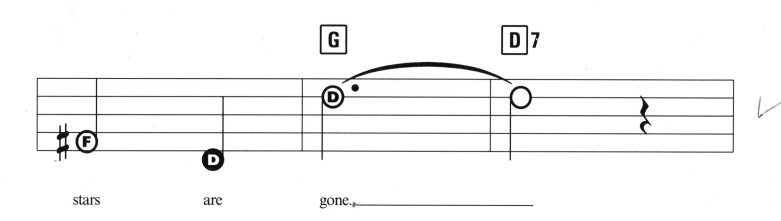

stars are gone.

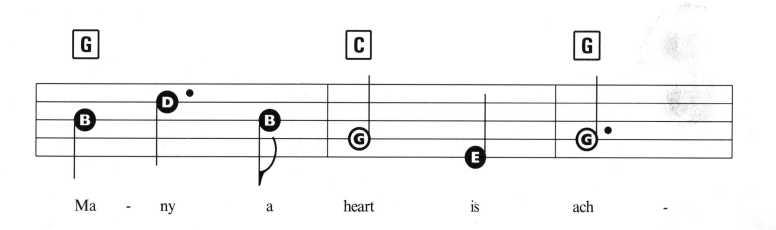

Ma - ny a heart is ach -

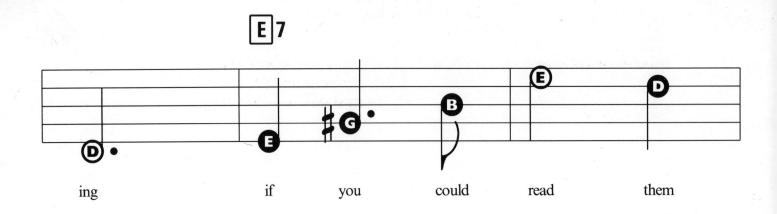

ing   if   you   could   read   them

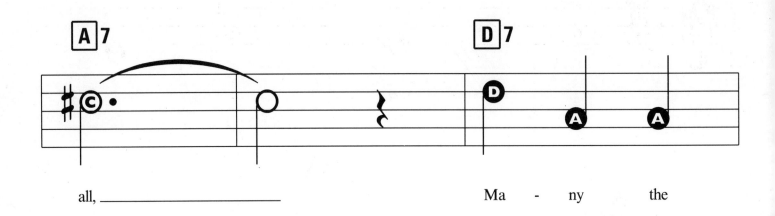

all, _____   Ma - ny   the

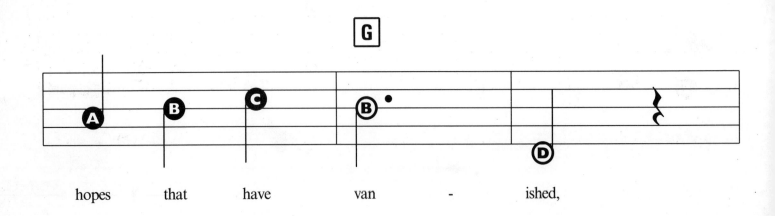

hopes   that   have   van -   ished,

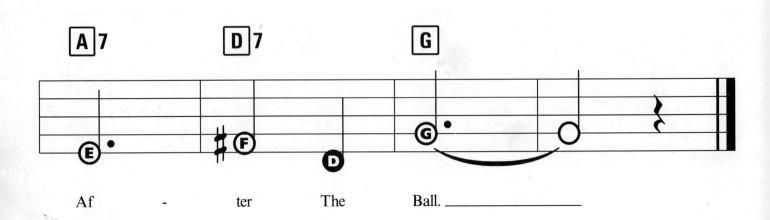

Af - ter   The   Ball. _____

Once Upon A Dream

Words & Music by
Sammy Fain & Jack Lawrence

Suggested Registration: Saxophone or Strings

Rhythm: Waltz

Tempo: Fast

Technique: Fast Waltz tempo

Sharps and Flats. ♯ ♭

Diminished chords A♭dim F♯dim

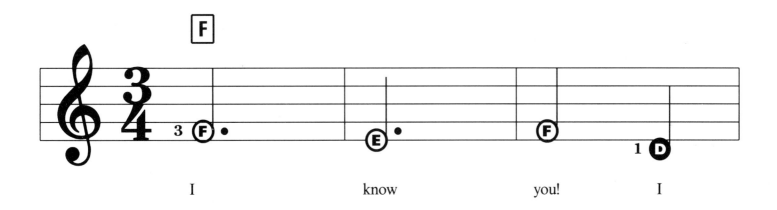

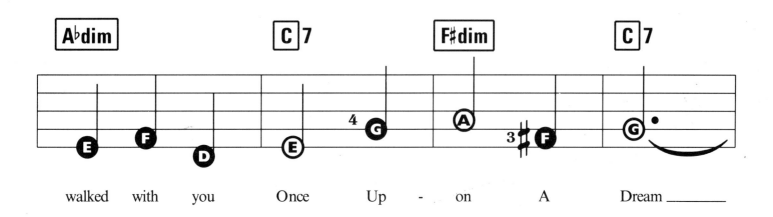

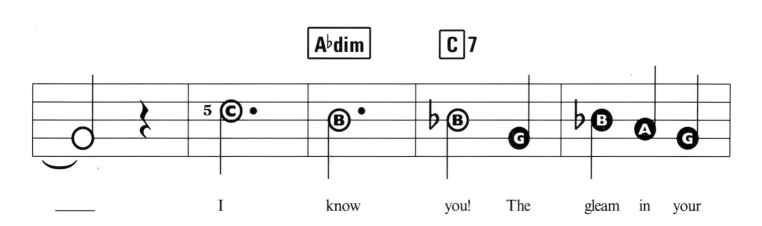

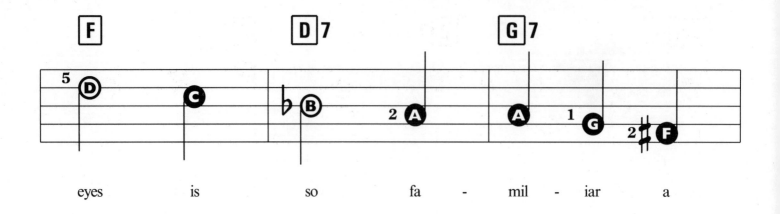

eyes   is   so   fa - mil - iar   a

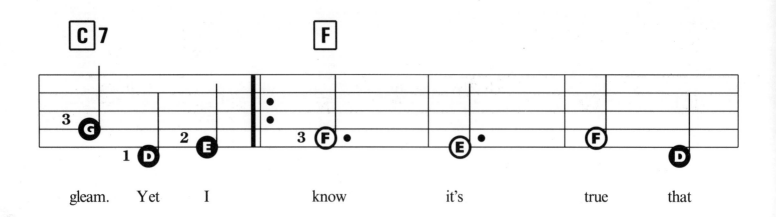

gleam.   Yet   I   know   it's   true   that

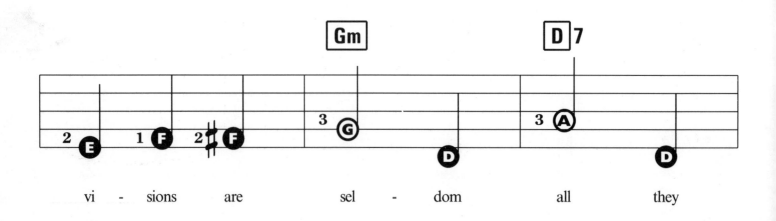

vi - sions   are   sel - dom   all   they

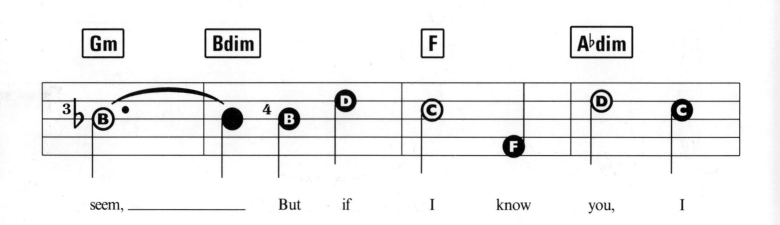

seem, _____ But   if   I   know   you,   I

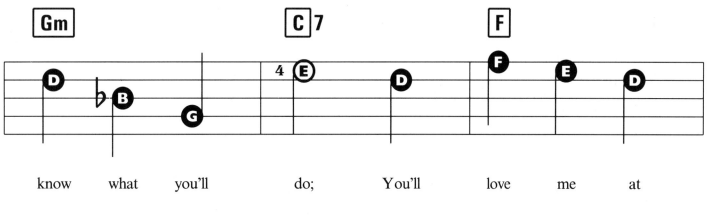

know   what   you'll   do;   You'll   love   me   at

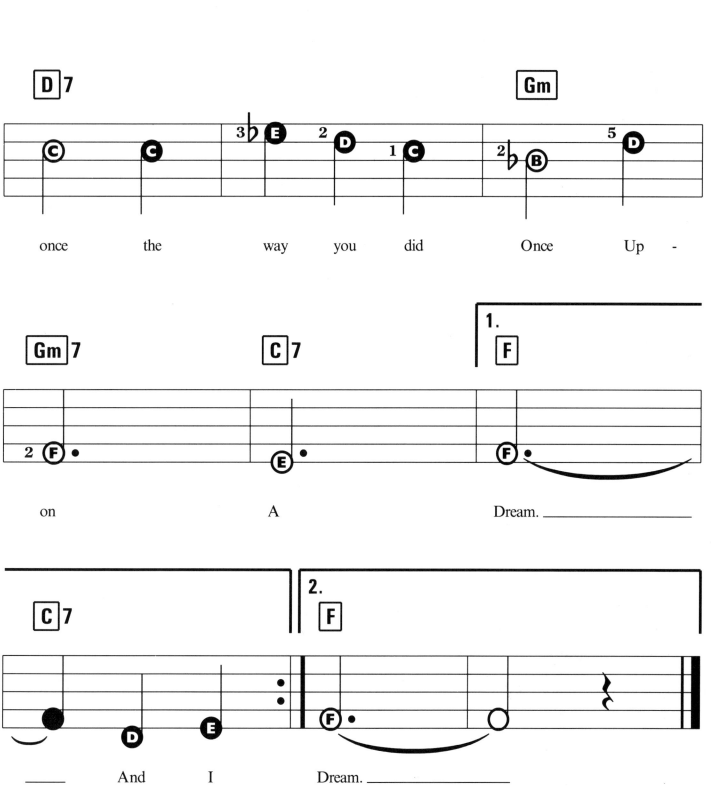

once   the   way   you   did   Once   Up -

on   A   Dream. _____

_____   And   I   Dream. _____

Prelude

Composed by Frederik Chopin

Suggested Registration: Piano or Strings

Rhythm: Waltz

Tempo: Medium Slow

Technique: Dotted eighth note – sixteenth note phrases.

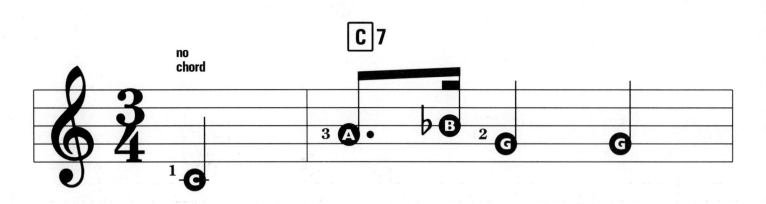

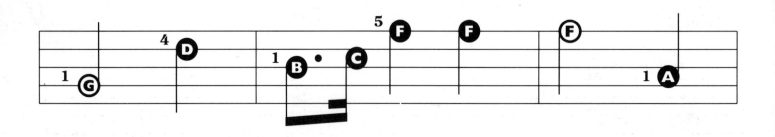

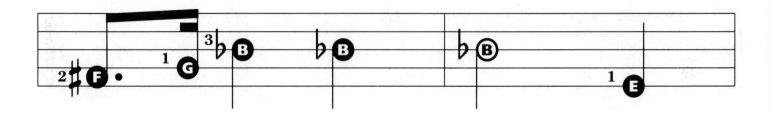

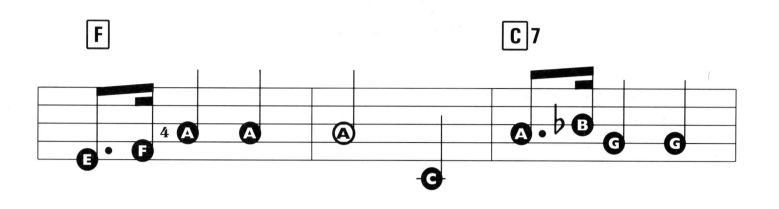

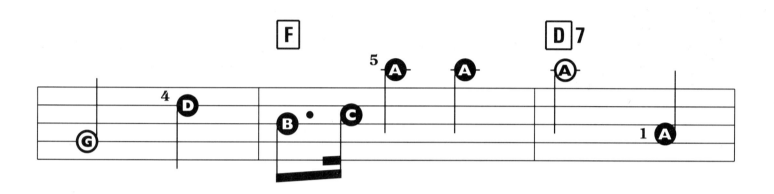

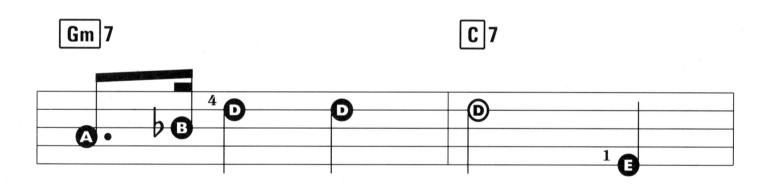

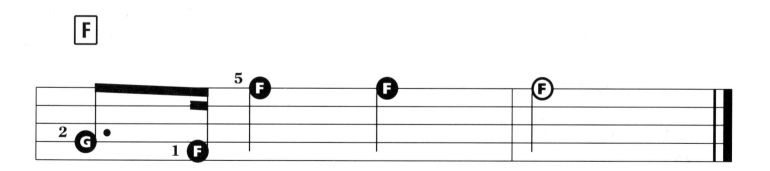

Swedish Rhapsody (Midsummer Vigil)

Based on themes by Hugo Alfven
Adaptation by Percy Faith

Suggested Registration: Strings or Celeste

Rhythm: Swing or Polka

Tempo: Medium

Technique: Eighth note phrases

Repeat section, and D.C. al Coda

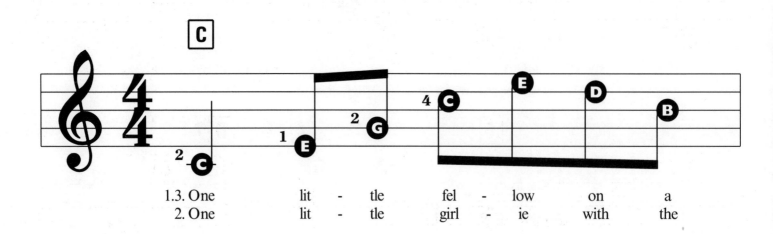

1.3. One lit - tle fel - low on a
2. One lit - tle girl - ie with the

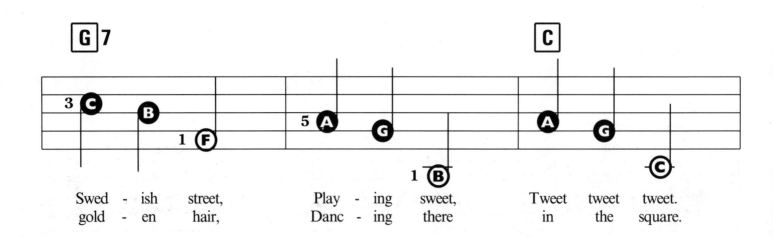

Swed - ish street, Play - ing sweet, Tweet tweet tweet.
gold - en hair, Danc - ing there in the square.

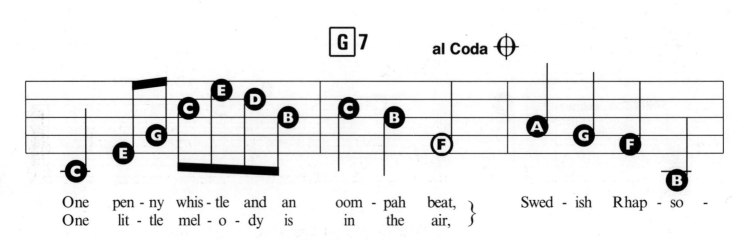

One pen - ny whis - tle and an oom - pah beat, } Swed - ish Rhap - so -
One lit - tle mel - o - dy is in the air, }

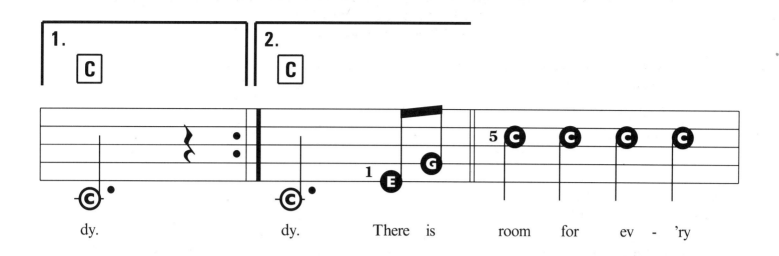

dy.   dy.   There   is   room   for   ev - 'ry

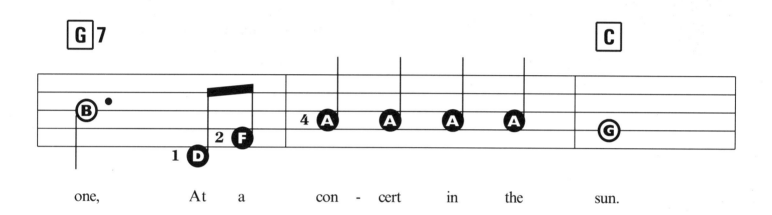

one,   At   a   con - cert   in   the   sun.

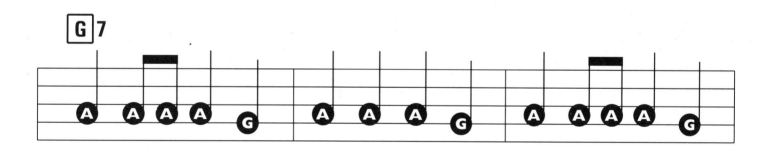

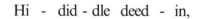

Hi - did - dle deed - in,   Go   to   Swed - en,   If   you   are need - in'

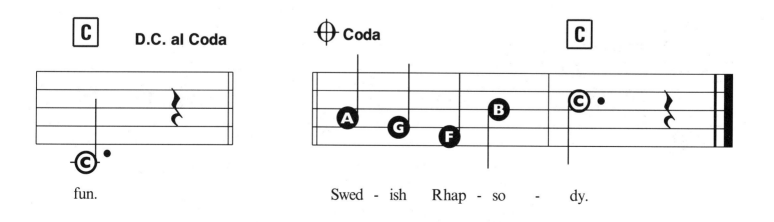

D.C. al Coda

Coda

fun.   Swed - ish   Rhap - so - dy.

Tales From The Vienna Woods

Composed by Johann Strauss

Suggested Registration: Strings or Vibraphone

Rhythm: Waltz

Tempo: Medium Fast

Technique: Dotted eighth note phrases

Tied notes

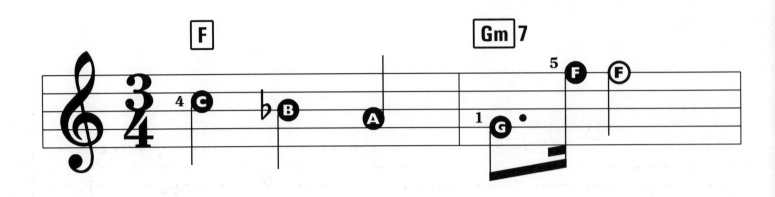

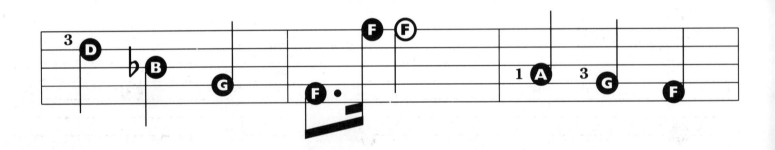

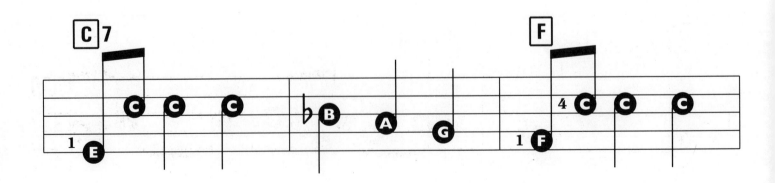

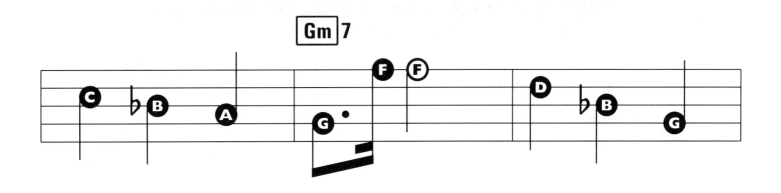

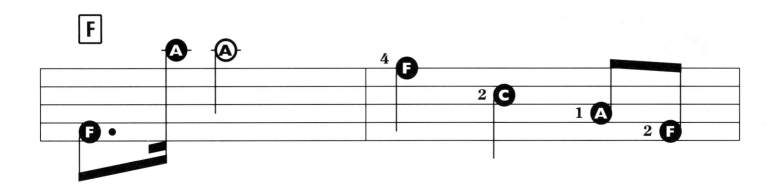

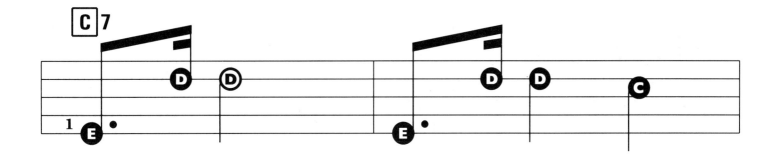

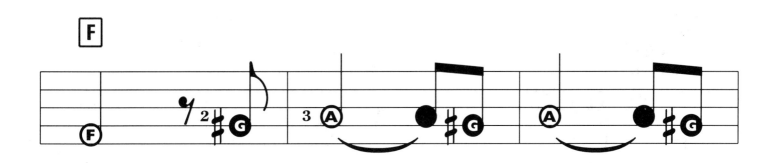

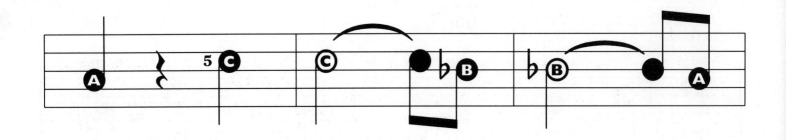

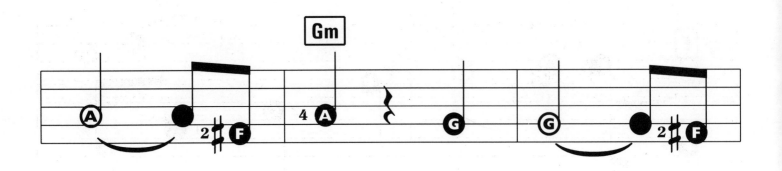

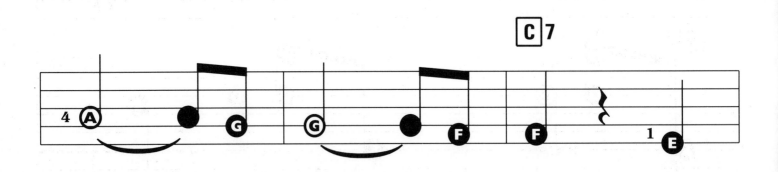

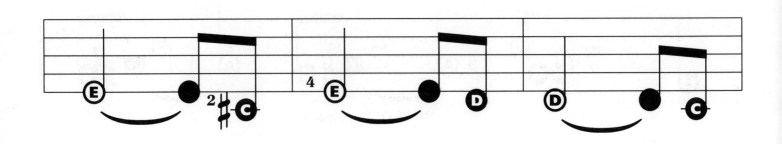

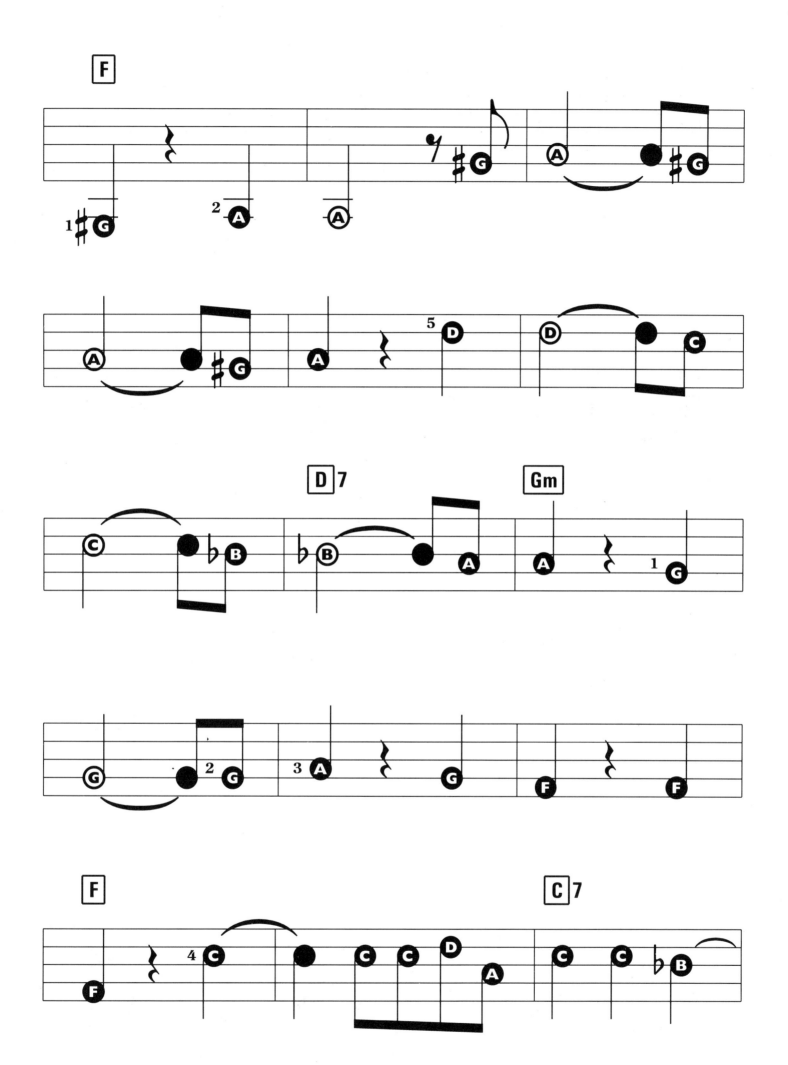

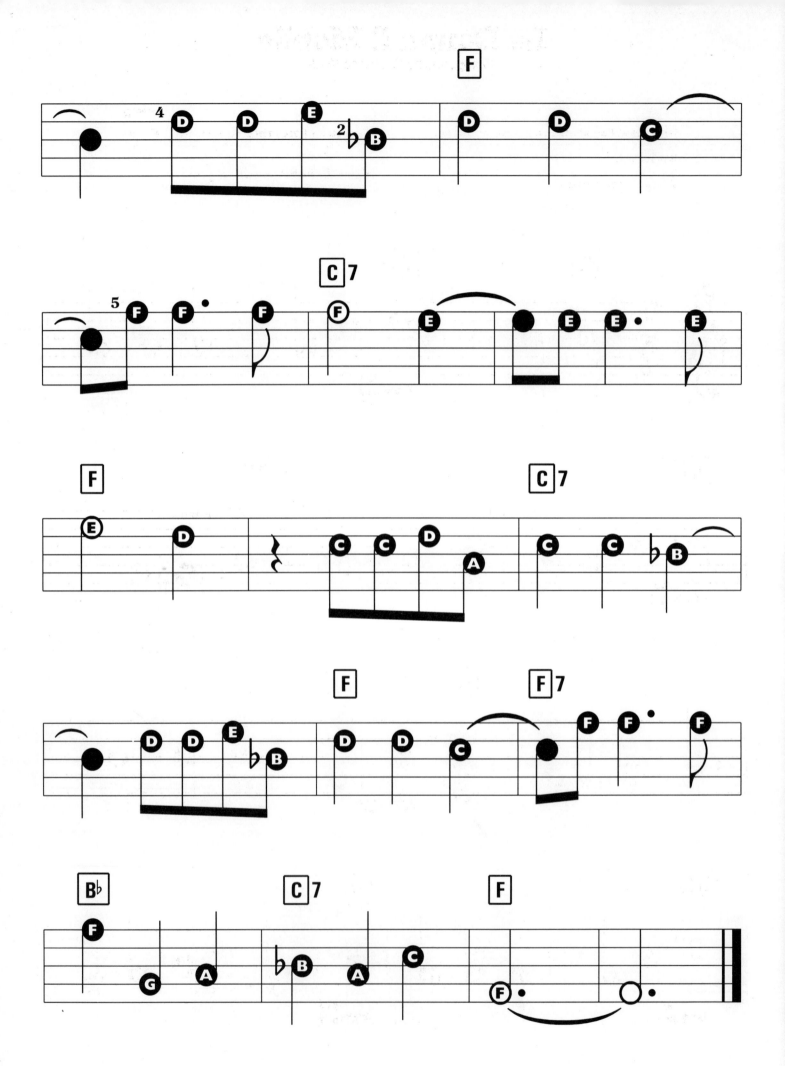

Le Donna E Mobile

Composed by Giuseppe Verdi

Suggested Registration: Accordion or Trumpet

Rhythm: Waltz

Tempo: Medium Fast

Technique: Dotted eighth note phrases

Eighth note triplets

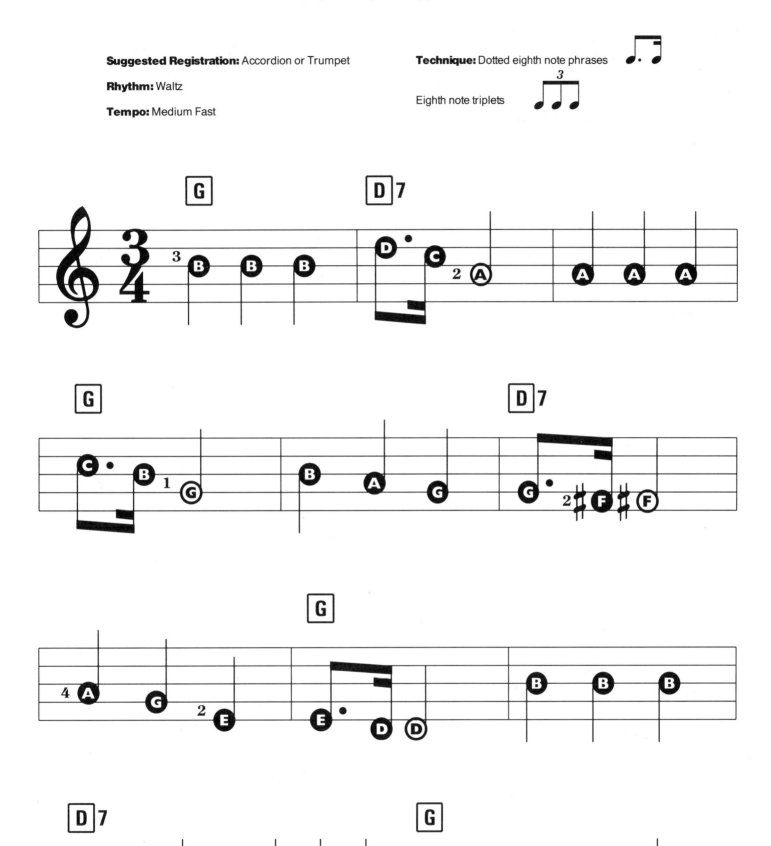

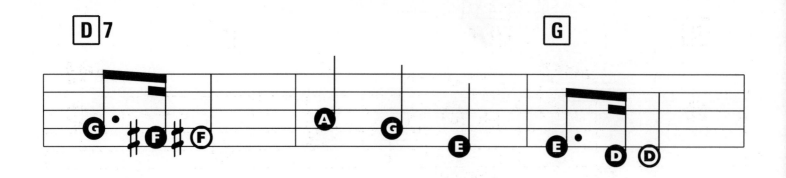

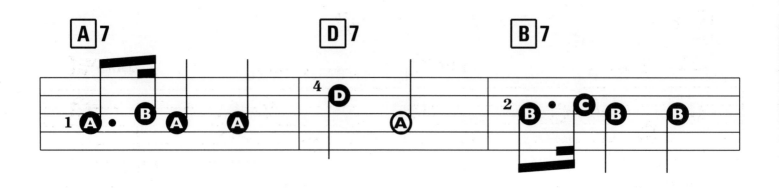

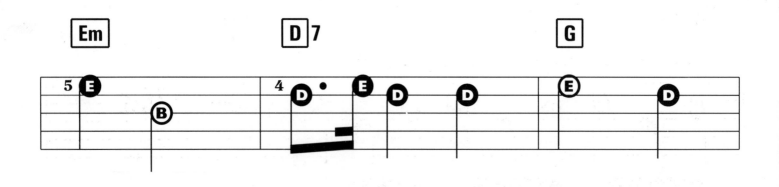

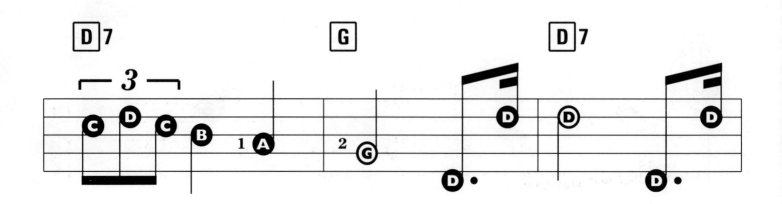

20

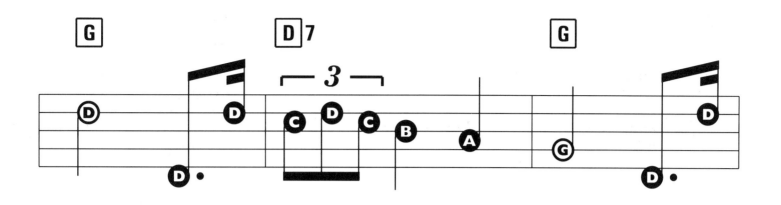

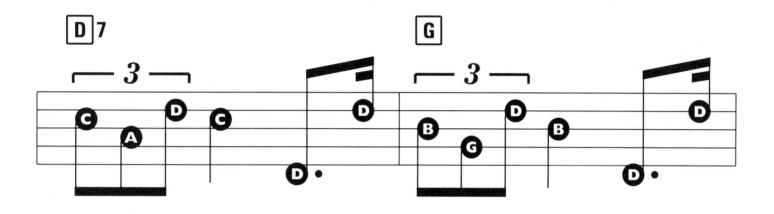

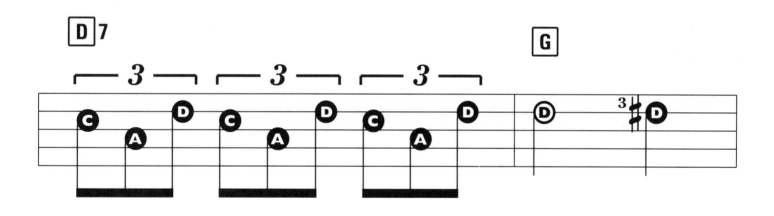

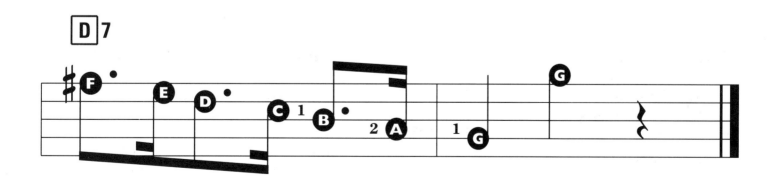

Hey Jealous Lover

Words & Music by
Sammy Cahn, Kay Twomey & Bee Walker

Suggested Registration: Piano or Vibraphone

Rhythm: Swing

Tempo: Medium

Technique: Augmented and diminished chords

Gaug E♭dim C#dim

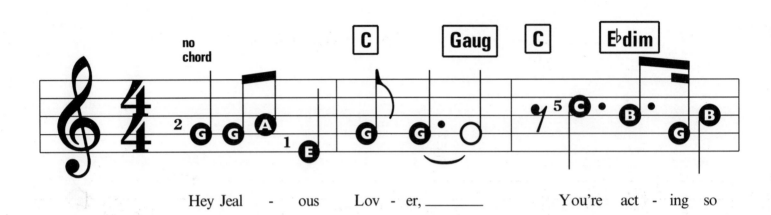

Hey Jeal - ous Lov - er, _____ You're act - ing so

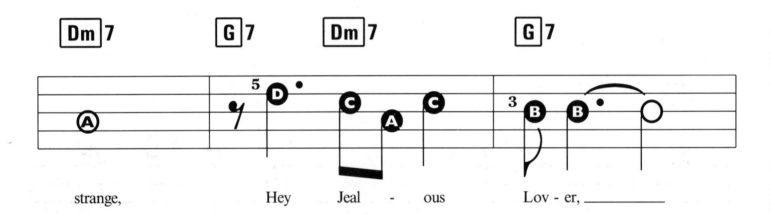

strange, Hey Jeal - ous Lov - er, _____

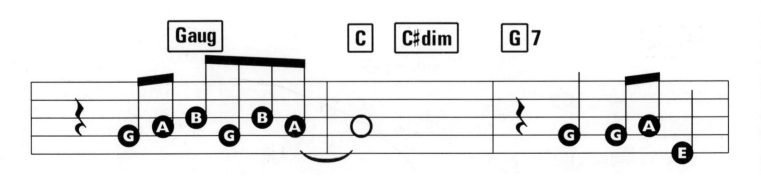

What is mak - ing you change? _____ Hey Jeal - ous

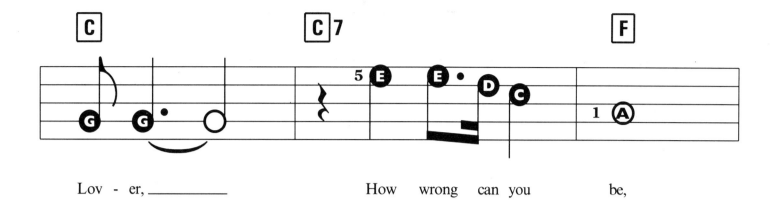

Lov - er, _____ How wrong can you be,

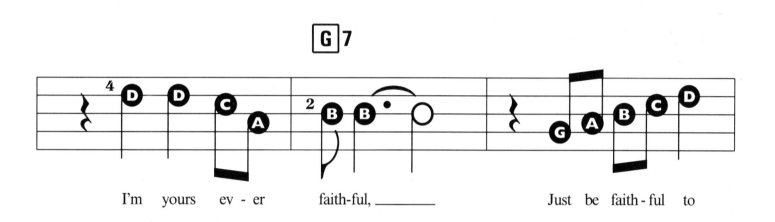

I'm yours ev - er faith-ful, _____ Just be faith-ful to

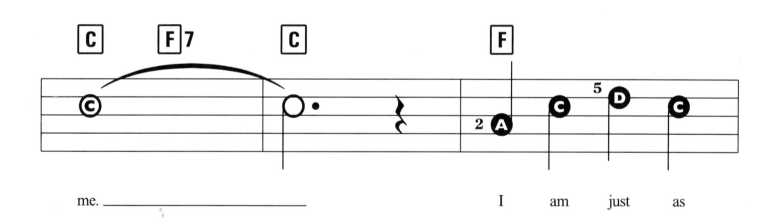

me. _____ I am just as

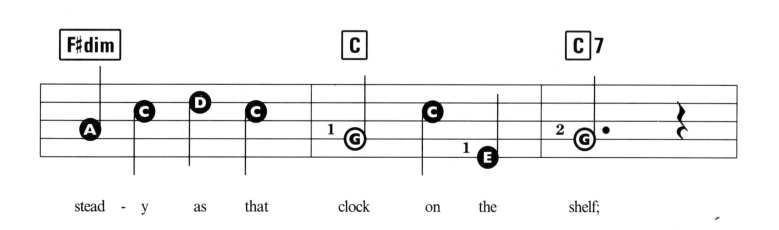

stead - y as that clock on the shelf;

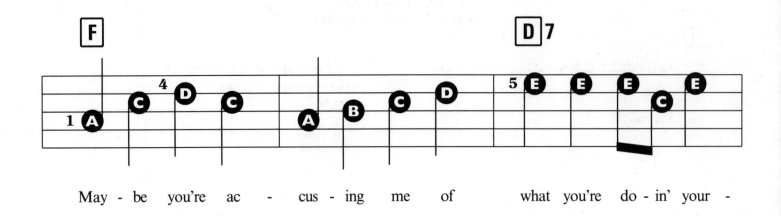

May - be you're ac - cus - ing me of what you're do - in' your -

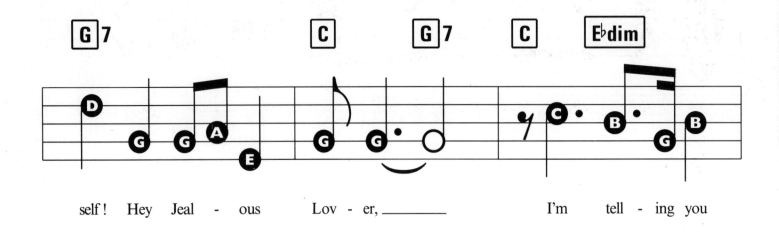

self! Hey Jeal - ous Lov - er, _____ I'm tell - ing you

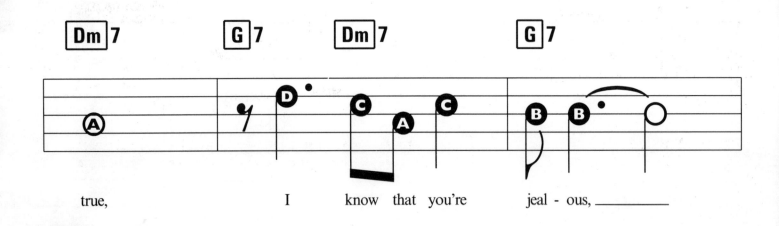

true, I know that you're jeal - ous, _____

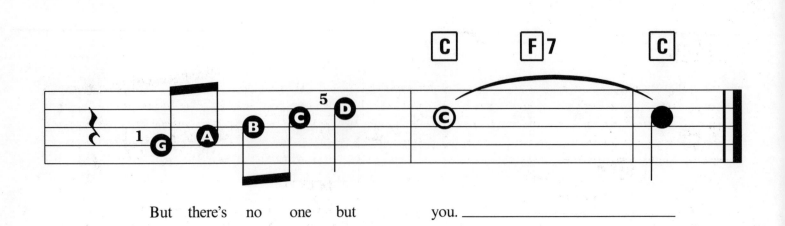

But there's no one but you. _____

More Than I Can Say

Words & Music by
Sonny Curtis & Jerry Allison

Suggested Registration: Elec. Guitar or Piano

Rhythm: Rock (8 beat) or Latin

Tempo: Medium

Technique: Sixteenth note phrases, to be played in a smooth lyrical style.

Yea.___

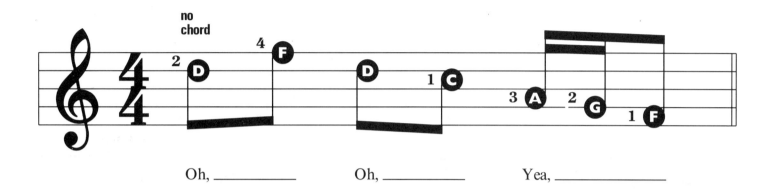

Oh, _____   Oh, _____   Yea, _____

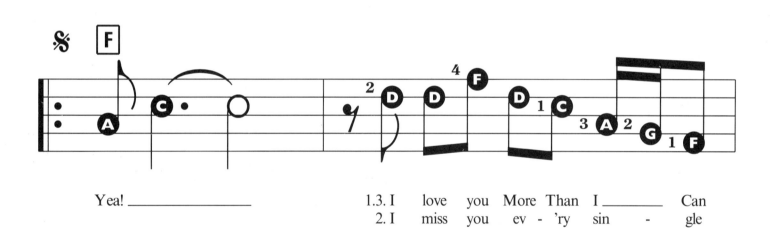

Yea! _____

1.3. I   love   you   More   Than   I _____   Can
2. I   miss   you   ev - 'ry   sin - gle

Say. _____
day. _____

I'll   love   you   twice   as   much   to -
Why   must   my   life   be   filled   with

al Coda

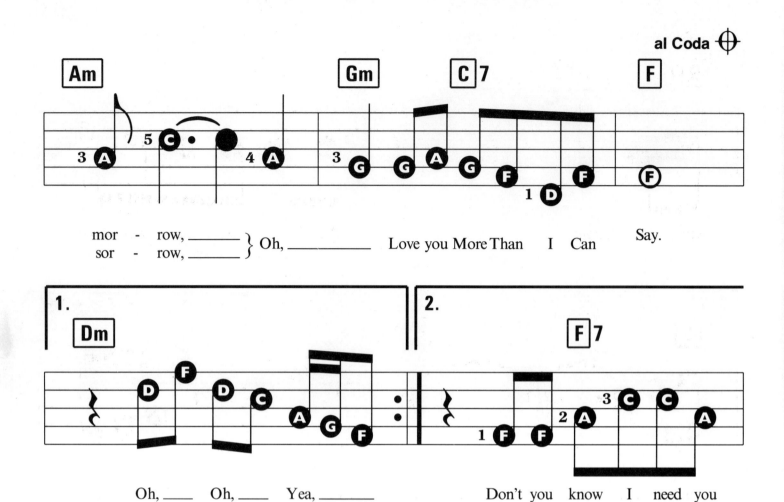

mor - row, _____ } Oh, _____ Love you More Than I Can Say.

sor - row, _____

Oh, ___ Oh, ___ Yea, _____   Don't you know I need you

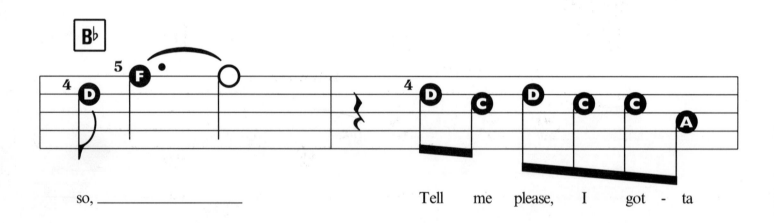

so, _____   Tell me please, I got - ta

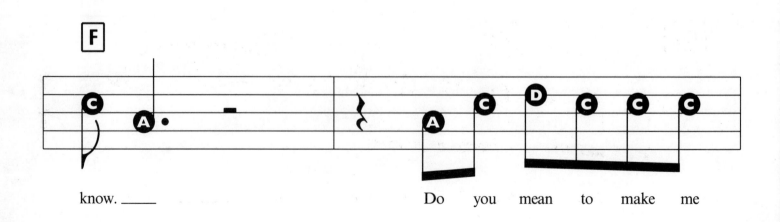

know. ____   Do you mean to make me

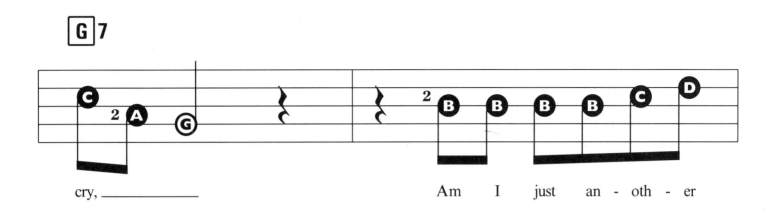

cry, _____   Am   I   just   an - oth - er

D.S. al Coda

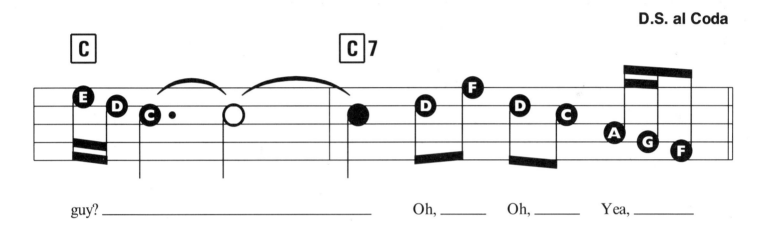

guy? _____   Oh, ____   Oh, ____   Yea, ____

⊕ **Coda**

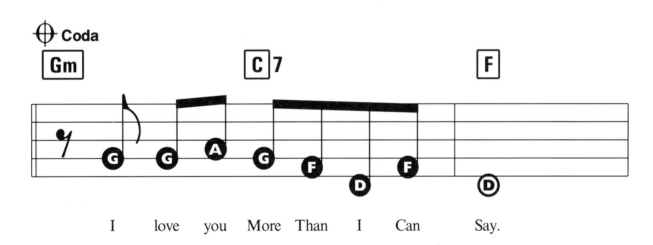

I   love   you   More   Than   I   Can   Say.

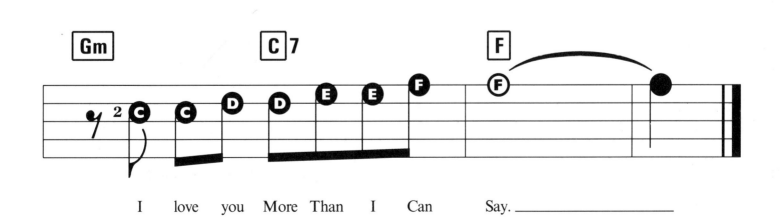

I   love   you   More   Than   I   Can   Say. _____

27

Time Was

English Lyric by S.K. Russell
Music by Miquel Prado

Suggested Registration: Trumpet or Acoustic Guitar

Rhythm: Swing or Beguine

Tempo: Medium

Technique: Quarter note triplets

Sharps. ♯

Diminished chords B♭dim Cdim Ddim

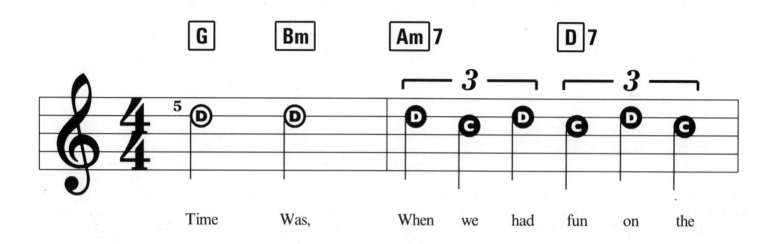

Time Was, When we had fun on the

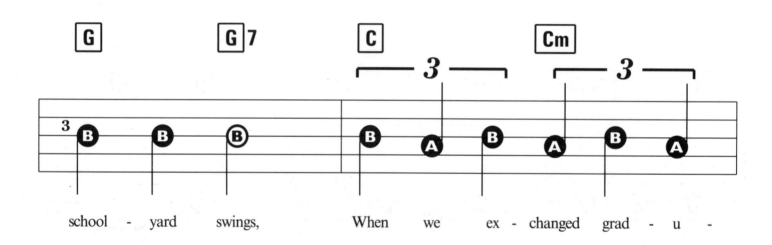

school - yard swings, When we ex - changed grad - u -

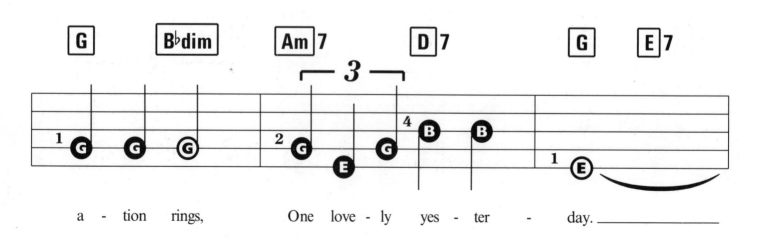

a - tion rings, One love - ly yes - ter - day. _____

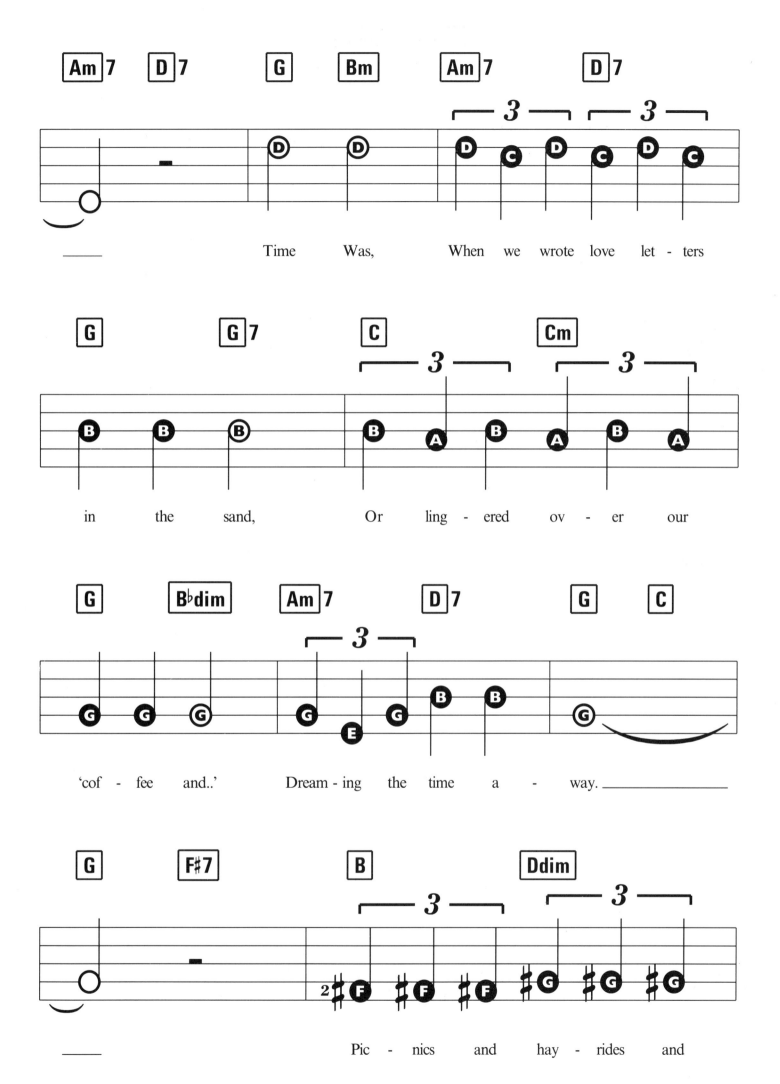

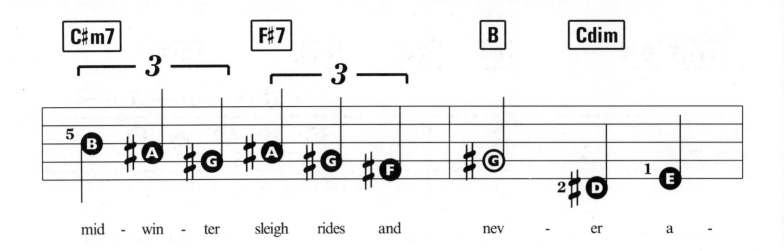

mid - win - ter   sleigh   rides   and   nev - er   a -

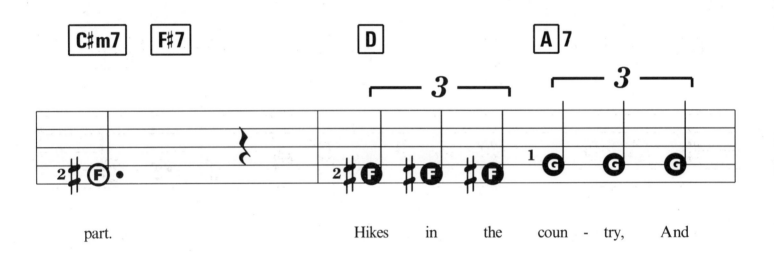

part.   Hikes   in   the   coun - try,   And

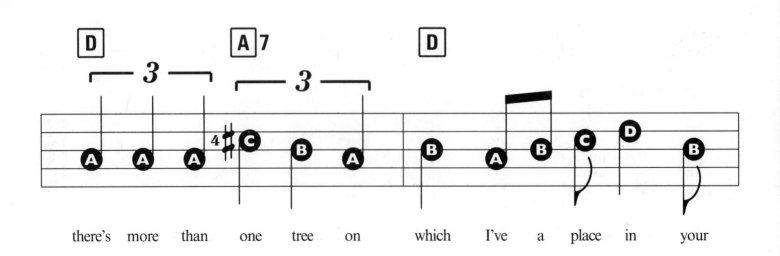

there's   more   than   one   tree   on   which   I've   a   place   in   your

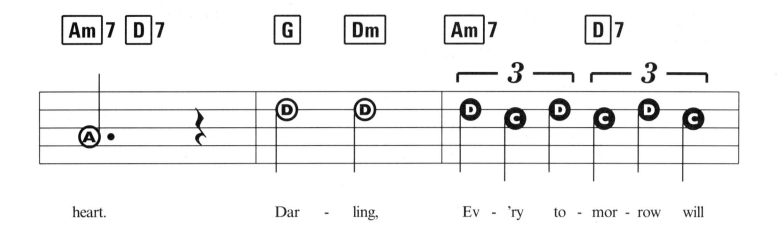

heart.   Dar - ling,   Ev - 'ry to - mor - row will

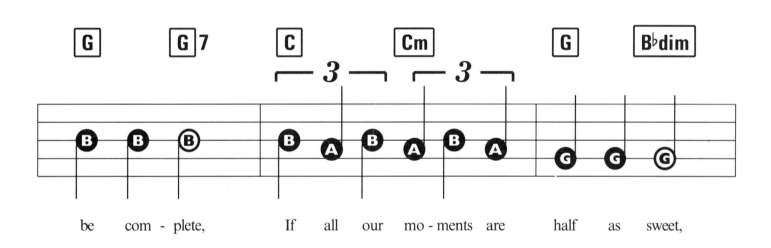

be com - plete,   If all our mo - ments are   half as sweet,

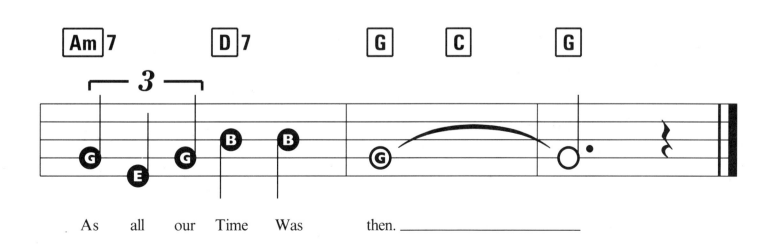

As all our Time Was   then. _____

If I Had You

Words & Music by
Ted Shapiro, Jimmy Campbell & Reg Connelly

Suggested Registration: Vibraphone or Piano

Rhythm: Swing

Tempo: Medium

Technique: Sharps & Flats. ♯ ♭

Note patterns ♪ ♩ ♪

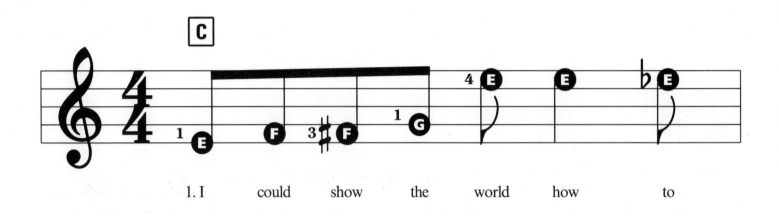

1. I could show the world how to

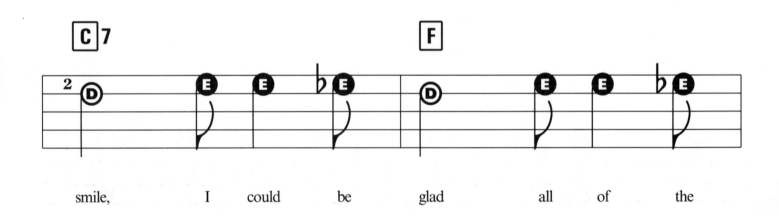

smile, I could be glad all of the

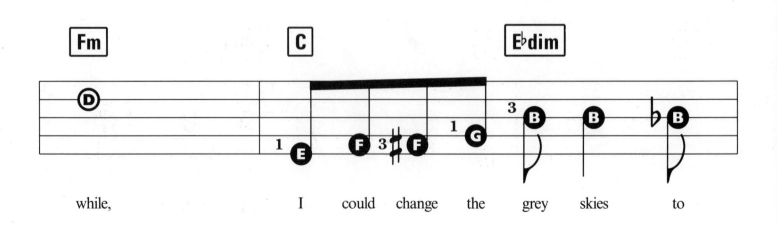

while, I could change the grey skies to

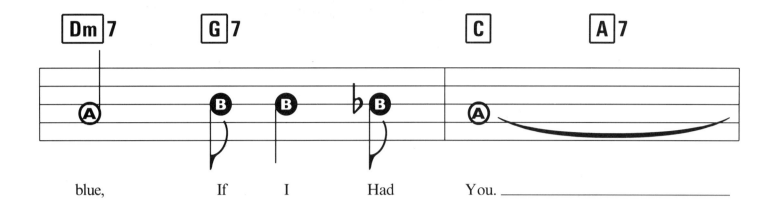

blue,   If   I   Had   You. _____

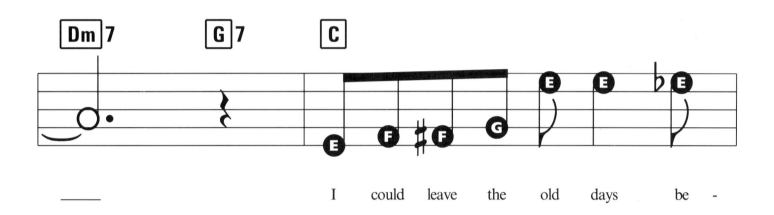

_____   I   could   leave   the   old   days   be -

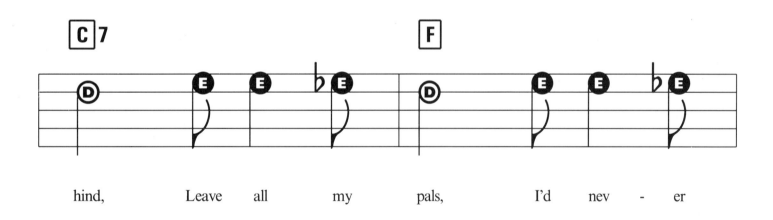

hind,   Leave   all   my   pals,   I'd   nev - er

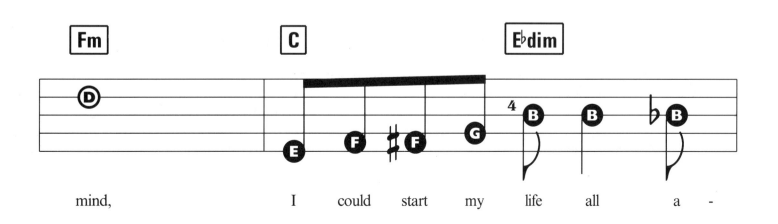

mind,   I   could   start   my   life   all   a -

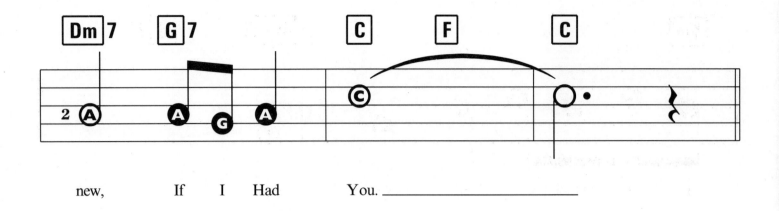

new,   If I Had   You. _____

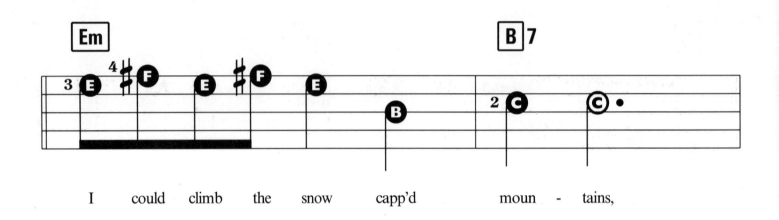

I   could   climb   the   snow   capp'd   moun - tains,

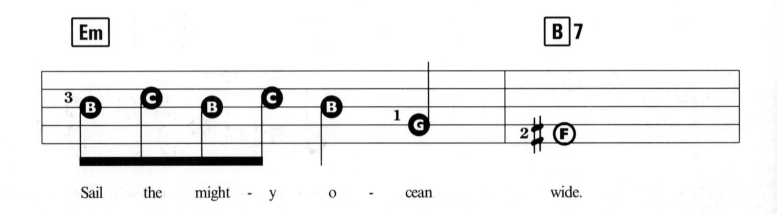

Sail   the   might - y   o - cean   wide.

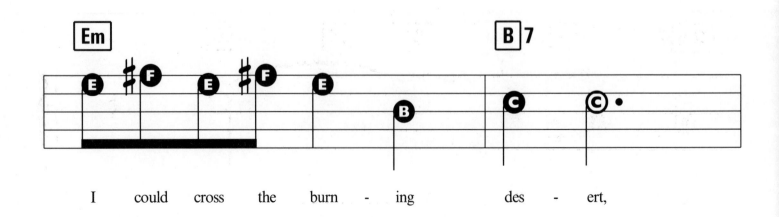

I   could   cross   the   burn - ing   des - ert,

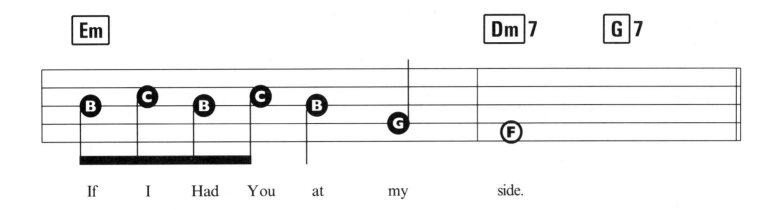

If I Had You at my side.

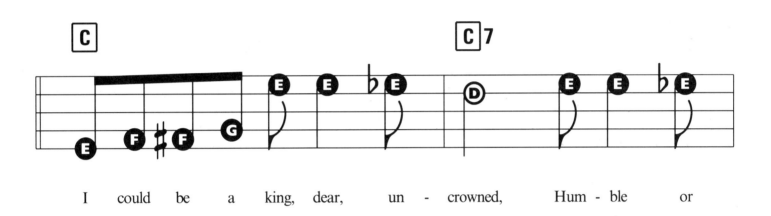

I could be a king, dear, un - crowned, Hum - ble or

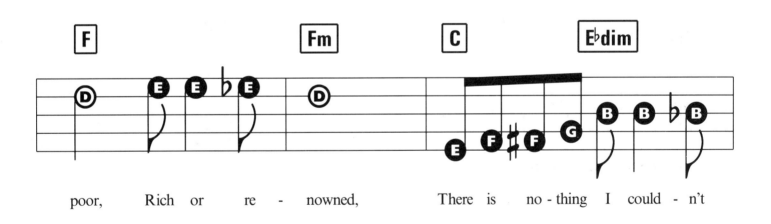

poor, Rich or re - nowned, There is no - thing I could - n't

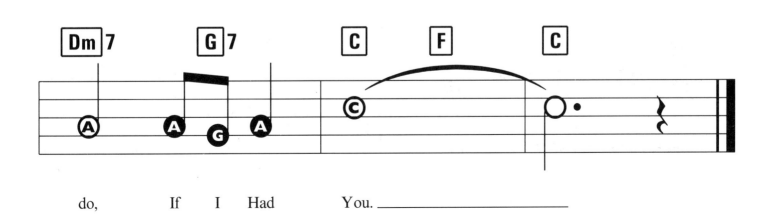

do, If I Had You._____

There I've Said It Again

Words & Music by
Redd Evans & Dave Mann

Suggested Registration: Flute or Trumpet

Rhythm: Swing

Tempo: Medium

Technique: Arrangement using 'To next strain' playing sequence with D.S. al Fine

Sharps. ♯

Quarter note triplets

Augmented and diminished chords.

Lyrics:

1. I love you, _____ there's
(2.) said it, _____ what
(3.) give me, _____ for

no - thing to hide, It's bet - ter _____ than
more can I say Be - lieve me, _____ there's
want - ing you so, but one thing _____ I

burn - ing in - side I love you _____ no
no oth - er way I love you _____ I
want you to know I've loved you _____ since

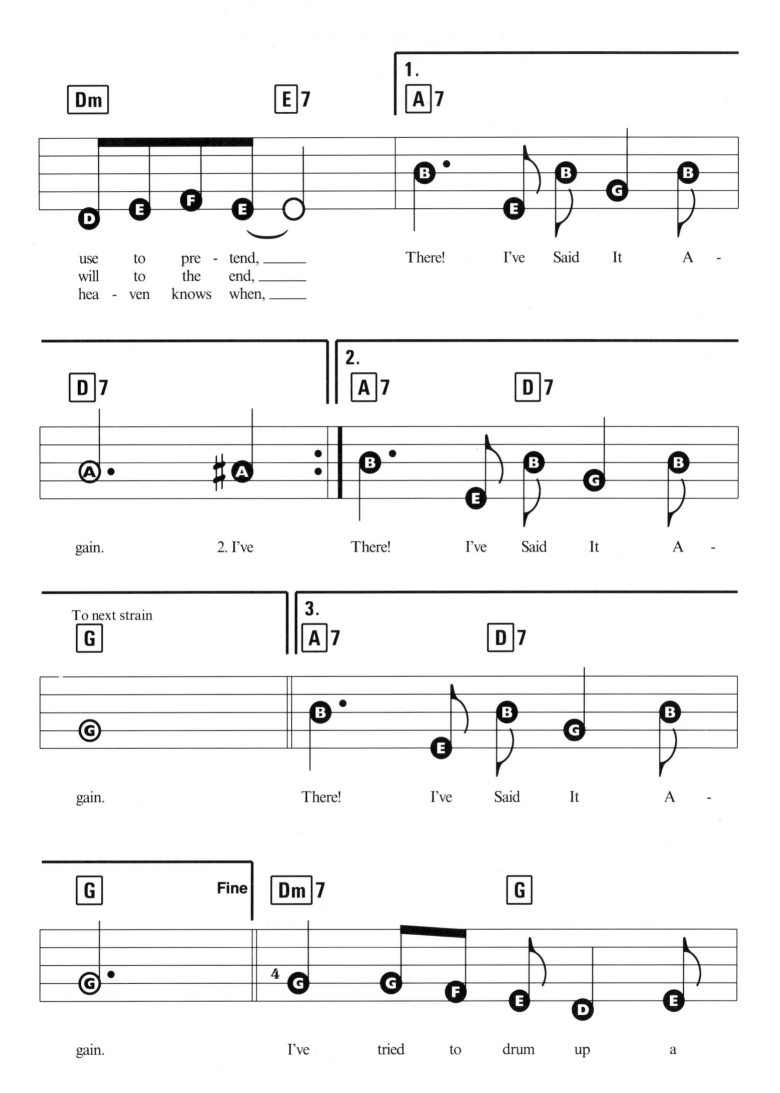

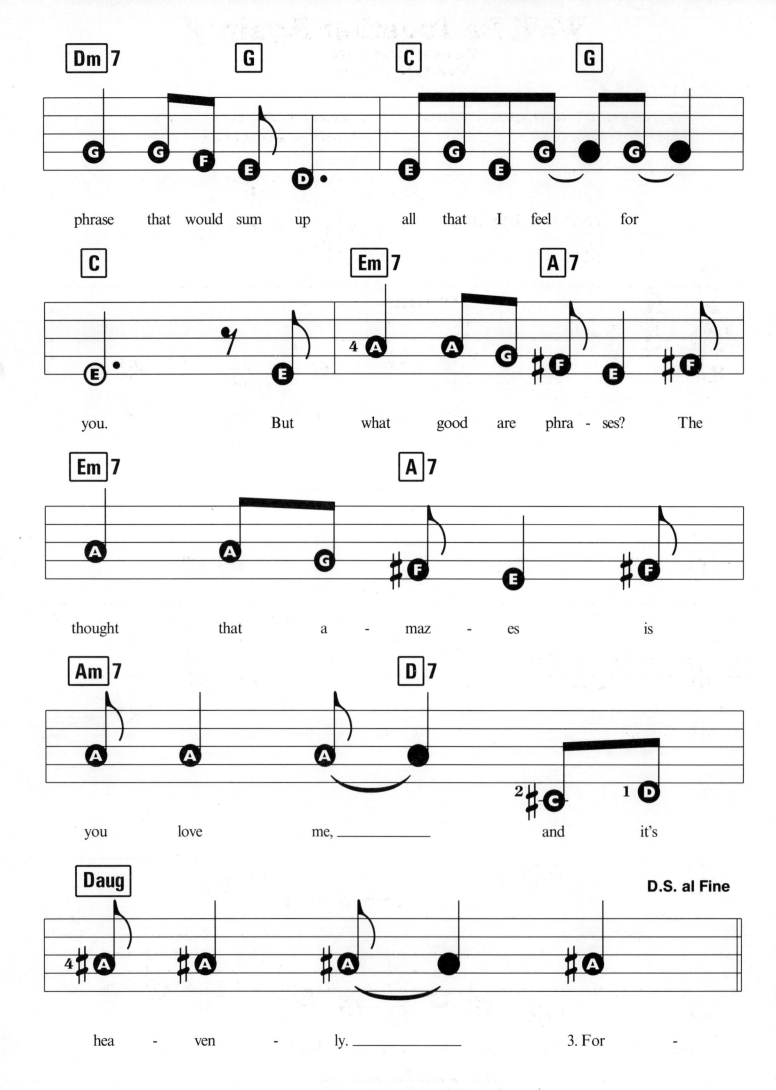

phrase   that   would   sum   up   all   that   I   feel   for

you.   But   what   good   are   phra - ses?   The

thought   that   a - maz - es   is

you   love   me, _____   and   it's

D.S. al Fine

hea - ven - ly. _____   3. For -

We'll Be Together Again

Words by Frankie Laine
Music by Carl Fischer

Suggested Registration: Vibraphone or Trombone

Rhythm: Swing (Ballad)

Tempo: Medium Slow

Technique: Verse can be played in ad lib style, with rhythm effectively added at Chorus.

Flats. ♭

Across-the-beat melodic phrases.

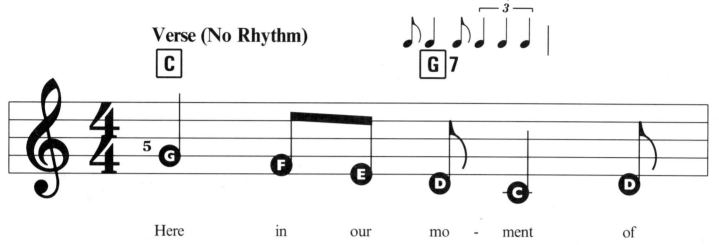

Here in our mo - ment of

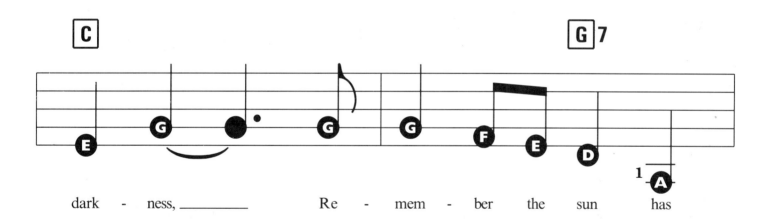

dark - ness, _____ Re - mem - ber the sun has

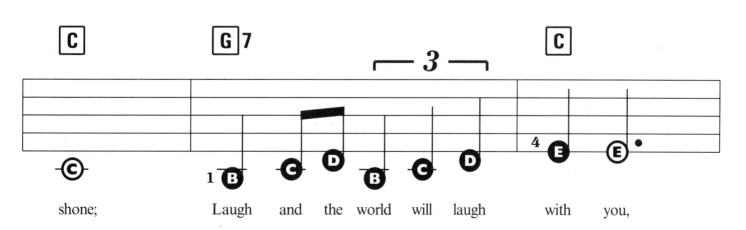

shone; Laugh and the world will laugh with you,

Chorus (Add Rhythm)

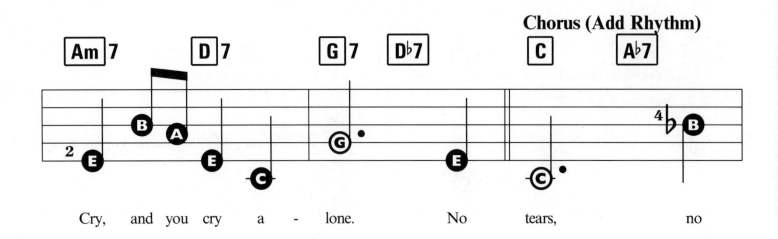

Cry, and you cry a - lone. No tears, no

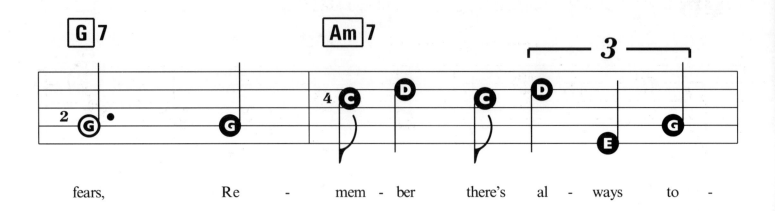

fears, Re - mem - ber there's al - ways to -

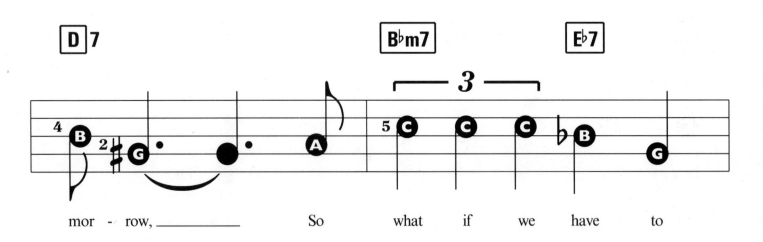

mor - row, _____ So what if we have to

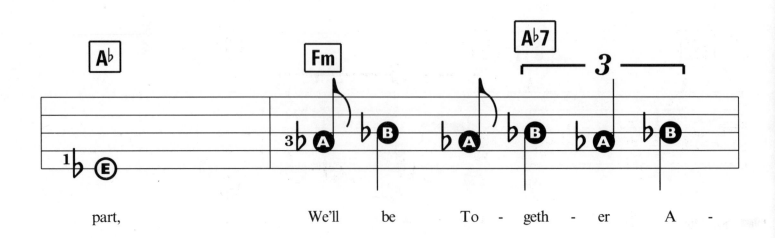

part, We'll be To - geth - er A -

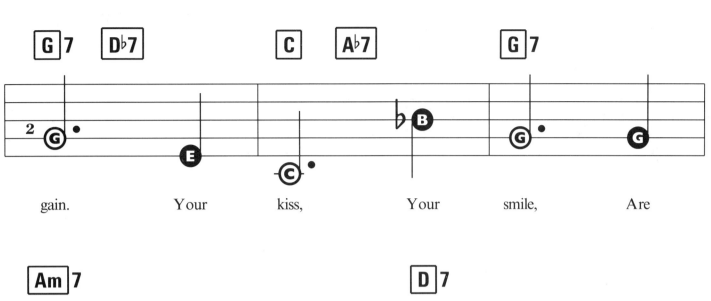

gain.   Your   kiss,   Your   smile,   Are

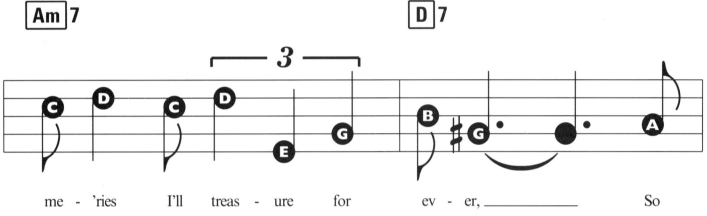

me - 'ries   I'll   treas - ure   for   ev - er, _____   So

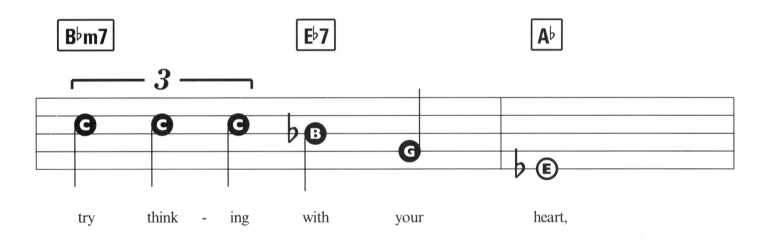

try   think - ing   with   your   heart,

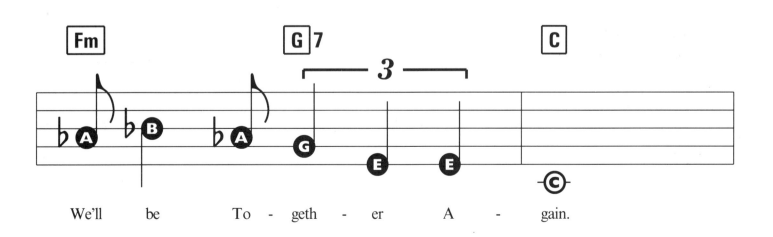

We'll   be   To - geth - er   A - gain.

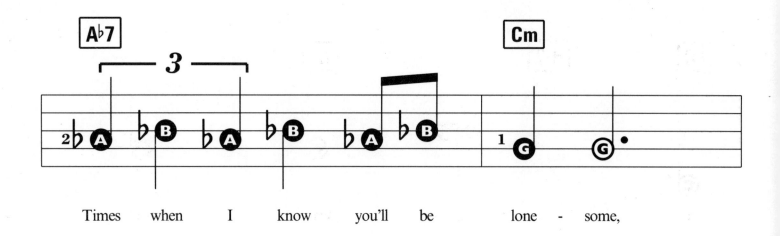

Times when I know you'll be lone - some,

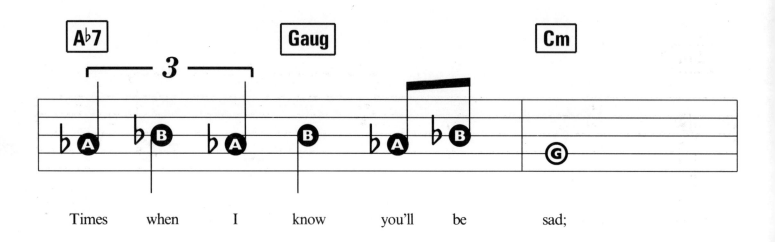

Times when I know you'll be sad;

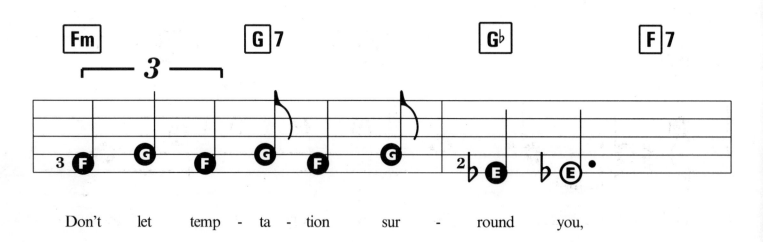

Don't let temp - ta - tion sur - round you,

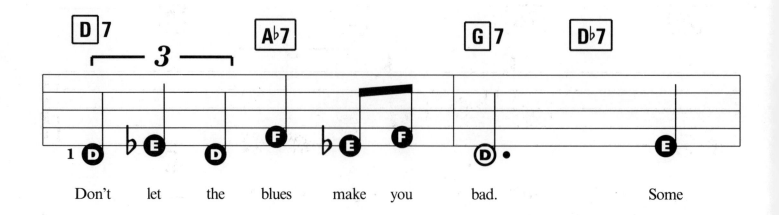

Don't let the blues make you bad. Some

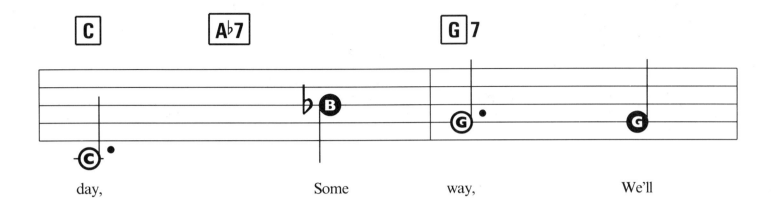

day, Some way, We'll

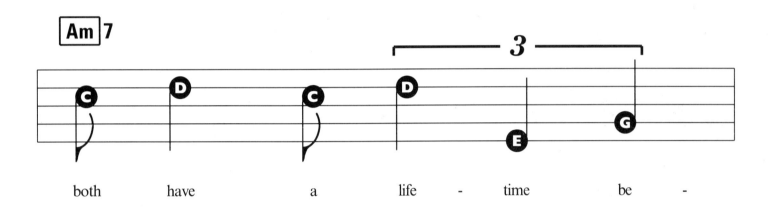

both have a life - time be -

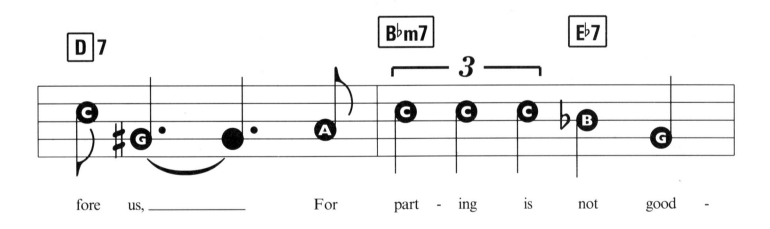

fore us, _____ For part - ing is not good -

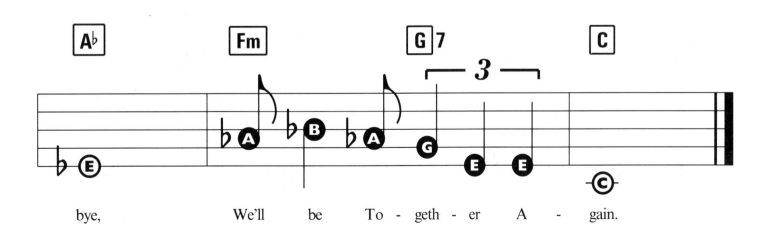

bye, We'll be To - geth - er A - gain.

Nice 'N' Easy

Words by Marilyn & Alan Bergman
Music by Lew Spence

Suggested Registration: Jazz Organ or Vibraphone

Rhythm: Swing

Tempo: Medium

Technique: Sharps and Flats. ♯♭

Augmented and diminished chords

Off- beat rhythmic phrasing

Cross fingering

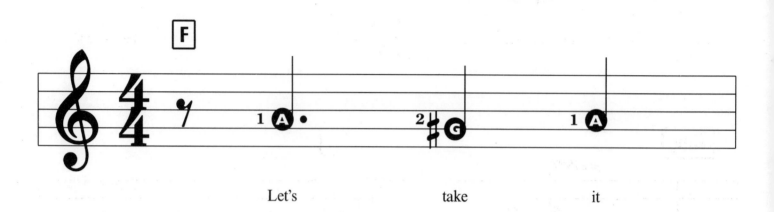

Let's   take   it

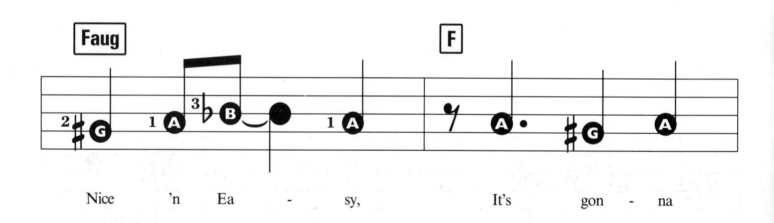

Nice   'n Ea -   sy,   It's   gon - na

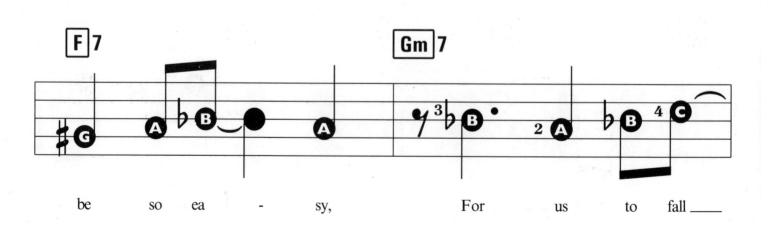

be   so ea -   sy,   For   us   to fall ____

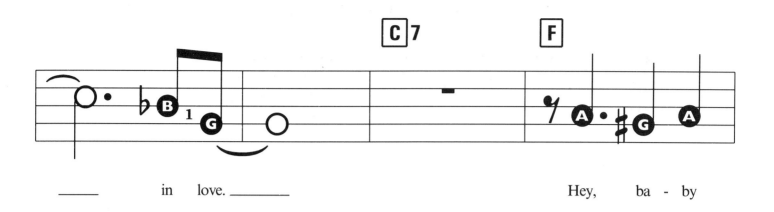

_____ in love. _____   Hey, ba - by

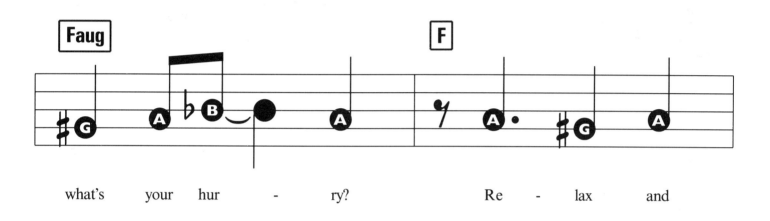

what's   your   hur - ry?   Re - lax   and

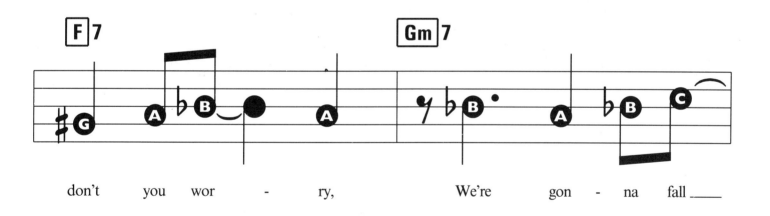

don't   you   wor - ry,   We're   gon - na   fall _____

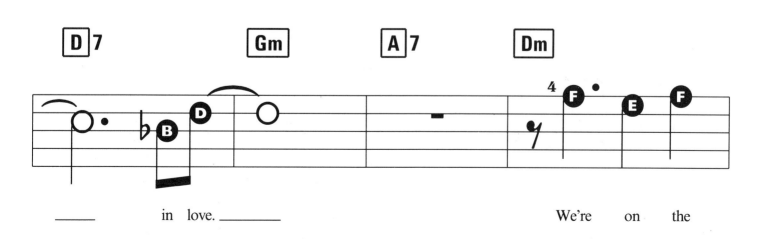

_____   in love. _____   We're   on   the

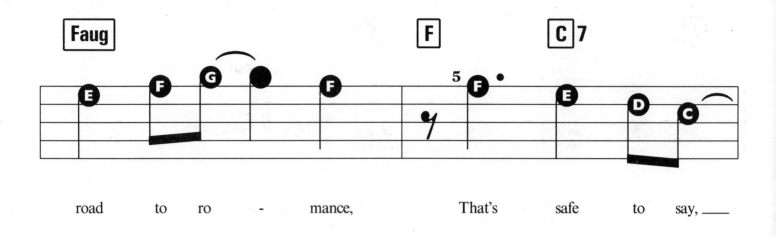

road   to   ro -   mance,   That's   safe   to   say, ____

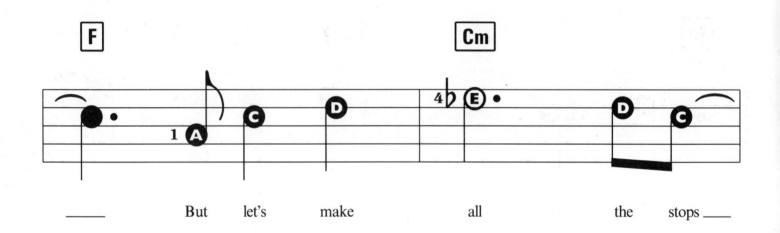

____   But   let's   make   all   the   stops ____

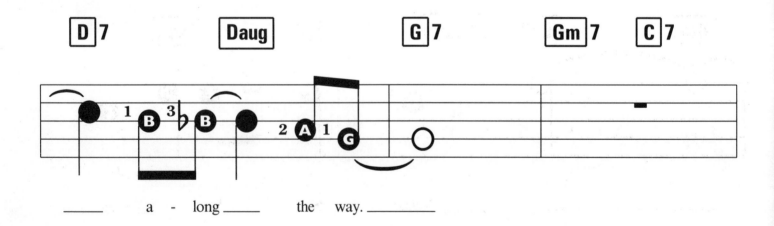

____   a - long ____   the   way. _____

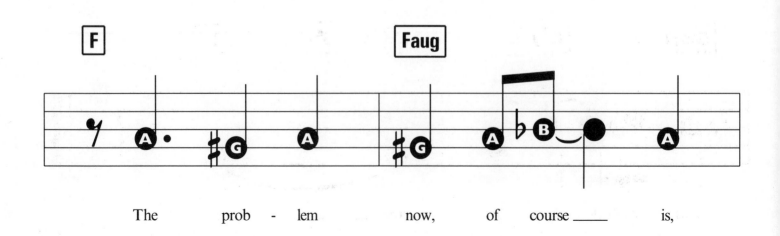

The   prob - lem   now,   of   course ____   is,

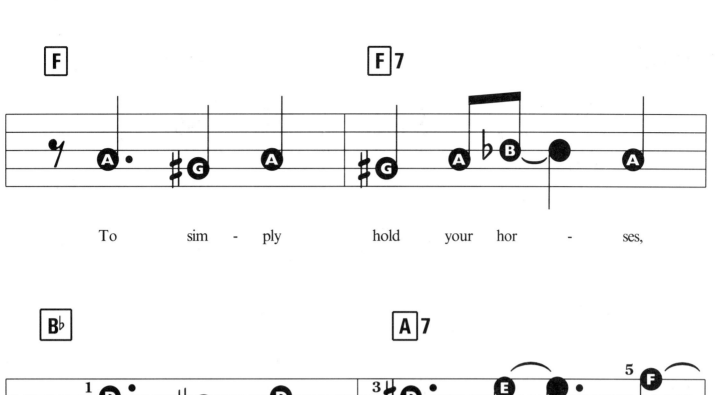

To sim - ply hold your hor - ses,

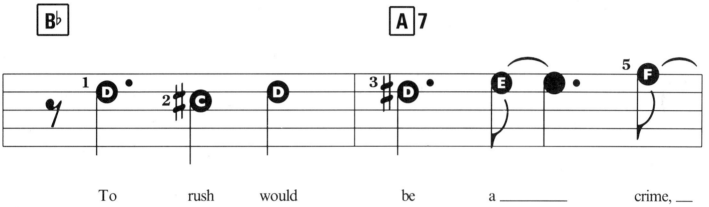

To rush would be a _____ crime, __

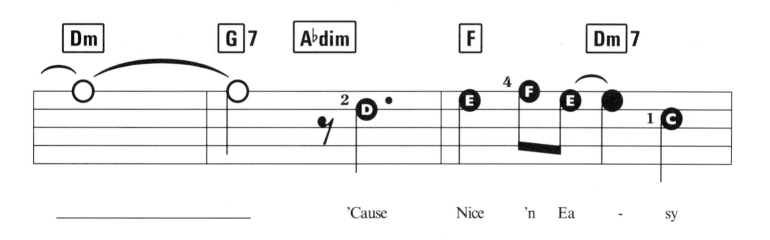

_____ 'Cause Nice 'n Ea - sy

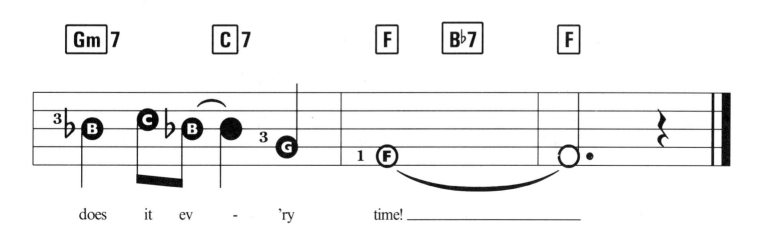

does it ev - 'ry time! _____

MASTER CHORD CHART

	Major	Minor	Seventh	Minor seventh
C	5 2 1	5 2 1	5 3 2 1	5 3 2 1
C#/D♭	4 2 1	4 2 1	4 3 2 1	4 3 2 1
D	5 3 1	5 2 1	5 3 2 1	5 3 2 1
E♭	5 3 1	5 3 1	5 3 2 1	5 3 2 1
E	4 3 1	5 3 1	4 3 2 1	5 3 2 1
F	5 3	5 3 1	5 3 2 1	5 3 2 1
F#/G♭	4 2 1	4 2 1	5 3 2 1	5 3 2 1
G	5 3 1	5 3 1	5 3 2 1	5 3 2 1
A♭	4 2 1	4 2 1	5 4 2 1	5 4 2 1
A	4 2 1	4 2 1	5 4 2 1	5 4 2 1
B♭	4 2 1	4 2 1	5 4 2 1	5 4 2 1
B	4 2 1	4 2 1	4 3 2 1	4 3 2 1

Diminished Chords.

C dim E♭ dim F#/G♭ dim A dim   C#/D♭ dim E dim G dim B♭ dim   D dim F dim A♭ dim B dim

4 3 2 1

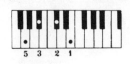
5 3 2 1

4 3 2 1

Augmented Chords

C aug E aug A♭ aug   C#/D♭ aug F aug A aug   D aug F#/G♭ aug B♭ aug   E♭ aug G aug B aug

4 2 1

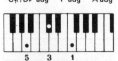
5 3 1

4 2 1

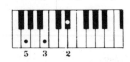
5 3 2